Next Patient Please

(A GP Remembers)

by

Terence G. Skinner

Published by

MELROSE BOOKS

An Imprint of Melrose Press Limited
St Thomas Place, Ely
Cambridgeshire
CB7 4GG, UK
www.melrosebooks.com

FIRST EDITION

Cover designed by Amanda Barrett

ISBN 978 1 906050 26 9

Printed and bound in Great Britain by:
CPI Antony Rowe, Bumpers Farm, Chippenham,
Wiltshire, SN14 6LH, UK

To my wife Hazel, my son in law Stephen, my daughter Sara
and my granddaughter Sophie

The Hippocratic Oath

I Swear by Apollo the Physician, Aesculapius, health, All-Heal, and all the Gods and Goddesses, that according to my Ability and Judgement, I will keep this Oath and this Stipulation: to reckon him, who taught me this Art, equally bear to me as my Parents, to share my substance with him, and relieve his necessities if required. To look upon his offspring in the same footing as my own Brothers, and to teach them this Art, if they shall wish to learn it, without fee or stipulation. And that by precept, lecture, and every other mode of Instruction, I will impart a knowledge of the Art to my own Sons, and those of my Teachers, and to Disciples bound by a Stipulation and Oath according to the Law of Medicine. But to none others. I will follow that system of regimen, which according to my Ability and Judgement, I consider for the benefit of my Patients, and abstain from whatever is deleterious and mischievous. I will give no deadly Medicine to anyone if asked, nor suggest any such Counsel. And, in like manner, I will not give to a Woman a Pessary to produce Abortion. With purity and with holiness, I will pass my life and practice my Art. I will not cure persons labouring under the stone, but will leave this to be done by Men who are Practitioners of this work. Into whatever houses I enter, I will go into them for the benefit of the sick, and will abstain from every voluntary act of mischief and corruption, and further, from the seduction of Females or Males or Freemen and Slaves. Whatever, in connection with my professional practice or not in connection with it, I see or hear in the life of men which ought not to be spoken of abroad, I will not divulge, as reckoning that all such should be kept secret. While I continue to keep this Oath unviolated, may it be granted to me to enjoy life and the practice of the Art, respected by all men in all times. But should I trespass and violate this Oath, may the reverse be my lot.

Author

My father was a dental surgeon. He worked his way up via office boy, rent collector and professional boxer. He started as a dentist in the days when you did not need a qualification, but merely bought the tools and a cylinder of nitrous oxide. Many times he would sally out at night with his forceps in his pocket and his nitrous oxide strapped on the back of his bike and do an extraction for half a crown (25p). Unfortunately, the law came in that decreed that all dentists must now take an exam and could then be allowed to practise as dental surgeons.

He was a practical man rather than an academic, and had many battles with examiners before he persuaded them that he was safe to be unleashed on the public; very much like my own progress through medical school.

By working all the hours that God gave, he made enough money to finance his lavish tastes, namely: polo, winning a medal at Olympia for show jumping, hunting with the Old Surrey and Burstow Foxhounds, point-to-point horse racing, and a single-figure golf handicap; not to mention three wives.

Here, then, was a man to take notice of. So, when I told him I wanted to be a musician and he said, 'Much better to go in for medicine and keep the music as a hobby,' one took notice. Indeed, the advice was absolutely right. However, I still achieved my ambition to play swing music in a dance band and even run a band of my own. But I had to wait till I was nearly seventy to get there.

If you ask most medical students what they want to do when they qualify, they will gaze steadfastly into the middle distance, with jaw set, and tell you, 'Surgery!'

They see themselves performing a delicate, life-saving operation on a rich, beautiful divorcee, while a pretty nurse looks up adoringly and mops the perspiration from his brow. The Judi Dench lookalike theatre sister slaps the appropriate instrument into the palm of his steady hand.

'Scalpel please, sister,' he commands in a firm but kind voice. Or 'Spencer Wells,' or 'retractor,' or 'whatever you think I ought to be using at this stage.'

I have spent many hours in operating theatres and have never experienced the temple-like atmosphere as seen in American films, nor the slapping of the instruments into the palm of the surgeon. The atmosphere is extraordinarily relaxed and the conversation revolves more around golf matches, holidays or the weather than the job in hand. The only time it goes quiet is when you open up the abdomen to find an inoperable situation and have to close up again quickly.

When I use the word 'you', I don't mean 'me'. I have never performed major surgery, nor am I likely to.

When I qualified in 1954, it was the end of an era when the old type surgeons were being mothballed and the new boys coming in.

The old surgeons worked very fast. Their initial incision was a rapid slash and their sewing like greased lighting. The new boys were very slow and meticulous but, nonetheless, very good. The reason for this was the advancing techniques in

3

anaesthetics. In the 'old days' chloroform was the anaesthetic of choice with a little ether thrown in; there was a small margin between surgical anaesthesia and death. Thus, it was desirable to keep the patient unconscious for as little time as possible.

With the advent of pentothal, pethidine and curare-like muscle relaxants, it was possible to get good surgical relaxation with a very light anaesthetic.

During one's student days, you had to consider which direction you wished to go in if you had the good fortune to qualify. As far as I could see, surgery consisted of repairing hernias, removing piles and appendices, with the occasional gall bladder to relieve the monotony. Medicine was very erudite and involved lengthy discussions about the patient sitting neatly in bed, in his best pyjamas, between starched sheets. Before the days of antibiotics, steroids and the cardiac group of drugs, there was actually very little in the National Formulary that influenced the course of a disease. Sir Alexander Fleming changed all that when he observed that a few spores, which had blown in through the window of his tiny laboratory in St Mary's Hospital, Paddington, had settled on an agar plate and were making inroads into a culture of virulent bacteria.

Not perhaps an earth-shattering event, you might think, but you've got to be pretty smart sometimes to observe the obvious.

Mark you, it took two more years for two Canadian scientists to produce penicillin on a commercial and marketable scale. 'Why Canadians?' we ask.

Outside the door of Sir Alexander's laboratory is a brass plaque notifying all who pass by of the momentous discovery. Underneath it, some wag has drawn a plaque-sized rectangle and written in it, 'WATCH THIS SPACE'.

Where was I? Psychiatry? Definitely NO.

Dermatology? Not very exciting. Whoever heard of a dermatological emergency? At least you never have to get out of bed in the middle of the night, as nothing is ever urgent.

Gynaecology? Rather limiting. After all, you spend your life treating an organ the size of a pear with two tubes leading off it to two walnuts. You can only do so many things with a uterus. Stick it back, scrape it or remove it.

Orthopaedics? No … crude carpentry.

Neurology? Strictly for the very bright boys. They spend weeks on tests and discussion, pontificating over a case so rare, only one had ever been described, and that was in Outer Mongolia. There was no known treatment anyway. There never is.

Roger Bannister became one of the country's leading neurologists and was subsequently knighted for his work, *not* because he was the first man to run a mile in less than four minutes.

We were both in the same year at medical school and he was an ideal target for experiments in the pathology lab. He would be made to run on the spot wearing a nose clip and breathing into a big bag on his back, after which, the oxygen was measured and his carbon dioxide assessed. What conclusions we came to, I haven't the faintest idea. He was one of the very bright boys, and a very nice chap.

What I do remember was that he had an incredibly slow pulse, actually, in the forties. Clearly this gave him massive reserve to run like he did.

I met up with him some 25 years later. He was presenting the prize at an athletic (ha! ha!) event. It was sponsored by one of the medical journals and invited GPs from all over the country to a 'Fun Run' round the old motor racing circuit at the Crystal Palace.

As I lived very nearby, I entered, and even went into training. I would go up to the track once or twice a week and lumber round the appointed distance. It was very hard work, and felt I wasn't doing myself any favours as I had a wife and daughter to support. So, a cunning plan …

Halfway round the circuit was a thick growth of trees and, by doing a sharp left turn, one could cut through a path and emerge back onto the track, cutting the overall distance by nearly half.

Come the day, there was a couple of hundred GPs limbering up in smart tracksuits and all wearing their donated GP JOG tee-shirts. I felt a bit out of it as most of my colleagues were obviously taking the whole thing very seriously. Most were wearing track shoes (I only had plimsolls) and doing vigorous warming-up exercises, which I found quite strenuous even to watch. I met an old colleague who had come up from Devon for the event, and we chatted on the start line until Sir Roger fired the starter's gun. My friend was off like a hare and, within the first 100 metres, I was a tail-ender. However, I got to my group of trees with a dozen or so obese gents and decided, 'This is it!'

Quick left turn and I'm in the trees on my well-trodden path, to emerge the other side, back on track to join my super-fit colleagues who were much too busy to notice my sudden inclusion. A few more hundred metres and I crossed the finishing line in approximately hundredth place.

My friend from Devon arrived very shortly after me. He looked at me in astonishment and said, 'I didn't see you pass me!' I tapped the side of my nose craftily and said, 'I'm a local lad. I know the course.'

The prize was a magnum of champagne presented by our celebrity. Naturally, I sought him out to say hello and recall some of the 4-minute-mile days. He looked at me and said, 'Good Lord, Skinner, you've put on a bit of weight!' I smiled deferentially and resisted saying, 'Et vous aussi, Sir Roger.'

Back on job selection. All the specialities rejected, only one left. GENERAL PRACTICE.

That's the job for me. My first choice. The infantry of the medical profession, the front line, the first assault on the enemy. Hot off the street, in their working clothes, or in their homes in their number two pyjamas. Admission to hospital necessitated a rapidly purchased new pair from M&S.

Let battle commence.

After 3 years as a houseman in the essential specialities, I considered myself ready to launch my skills on the unsuspecting public. Having got permission from the then Executive Council, I nailed my 'plate' to the gatepost, sat back behind my second-hand desk (acquired from a junk shop in Peckham) and waited – stethoscope and sphygmomanometer at the ready.

To my horror, a patient came in. He left after about an hour, impressed by the full physical examination to which he had been subjected, for what he thought was only a sore throat. I sat back, well pleased; only 3,499 to go, I thought; at that time 3,500 was considered a full list. Eventually my list went up to 3,600, 100 of which I rapidly axed as the Executive Council only paid you for 3,500.

Dr. Skinner 2006

The East End

To earn a crust in the early days when one's list (panel) was in single figures, like one's golf handicap, the more impoverished of us joined a set-up called Southern Relief Service. This was the first of the deputising services which provided cover for general practitioners for a few hours so they could recharge their batteries. In those days, one jealously guarded one's practice for fear that unscrupulous colleagues would try to woo them away. After all, £3.50 for the care of one person for 365 days (and nights) is not to be sneezed at. The sessions were for 8 hours. Mine was the night shift, 10pm to 6am, and I was banished to the East End, Mile End Road to be precise. I was given a grotty little room with a camp bed, blanket, chipped tin mug, a bottle of Camp coffee and, of course, a telephone.

I never saw much of the camp bed, nor tasted the coffee. Headquarters kept you well supplied with work. You went all over the place. If you did ten or more visits in one session, you would get a 10 shilling bonus (50p). This, on top of the fee of 30 bob (£1.50), was an attractive target. HQ were very adept at stopping you at nine, then feed in some other poor unfortunate to get what would have been your tenth. Amazing how many of us had nine at the end of a session, and how few the magical ten.

One night I was sent to a workhouse (yes, they did exist) and, looking for the front door, passed a queue of shabby down-and-outs. 'You won't get in there, mate, they're full up.' I did get in, however, having identified myself via a Judas Gate. What a place! Row upon row of doorless cells about 6ft by 3ft, with a bed and a blanket not dissimilar to my own back in the Mile End Road. The partitions were made of plywood and the flooring bare wood. I suppose this was five star luxury compared with the days when they slept on a clothesline.

When walking round the ill-lit backstreets off the Mile End Road, looking for Flat 7 D'Arcy Mansions at 3am, I was acutely aware that I was in Jack the Ripper country and that every bush or tree hid an assailant. I reassured myself that he and I were in the same profession, and that it would be most unprofessional to disembowel a colleague. In any event, with my black handed-down Crombie overcoat, slouch hat and medical bag, I am sure that, had I chanced upon any respectable prostitute, she would have run away screaming, 'He's back! He's back!'

In my nocturnal travels round the East End I found the people extremely courteous, polite, grateful and full of character. It was an environment in which I felt I could happily set up practice and work. However, my roots were in South East London and I'd only been banished here to earn my thirty bob because no one wanted to work the 10pm to 6am shift in this area.

I recall being called to an address in the small wee hours to a run down block of flats in Bethnal Green. You had to pick your way through rubbish and disgusting stairwells. You had the feeling that the whole lot was about to collapse. The lift door opened to reveal a most unpleasant interior, so I decided to walk the four floors. Interesting how all late night call outs are on the top floor and the lift not working.

I reached my target and was slightly confused by the door. It was bigger than standard and made of wooden planks with huge wrought iron hinges and an enormous black knocker. My tentative tap was immediately answered by a gent, half a head shorter than me but about twice as wide. He was wearing braces over a pristine white shirt, a sober but expensive silk tie, and was smoking an enormous cigar with the band still on. 'Good evening, doctor,' (it was 3am). 'Have you come to see my little lad? The missus will take you through.' I couldn't believe my eyes. Knee deep shag pile carpet, white leather suite, an enormous fish tank in which the angel fish could hardly find their way around for the bubbles. Two steps led up to a leather–fronted studded bar stocked with a variety of drinks from foreign parts, garish tubular lighting. On the bar, a monstrosity of a feature in which bubbles of varying sizes fought their way through, what I took to be, an oily medium. My questionable taste took a shine to this and I paused a moment to admire it. 'Gorgeous, ain't it?' said Mummy. 'We bought it in America when we were last there.' It was a few years before I saw one of these again; they began to grace many homes, usually having been donated as Xmas presents by teenage children. On past the bar, silk housecoat waving in the breeze, Mummy conducted me past the brocaded, tie-back curtains to the little lad's quarters.

Nice little chap, feeling very sorry for himself, and who's to blame him with an inflamed ear drum like he had?

Back through Aladdin's cave to the castle door. Monseigneur thanked me courteously and said he would have offered me a drink, but knew I was driving. I thought how nice to meet such a considerate, law observing citizen in an area where the Kray twins, the Messina brothers and the Sabini gang were plying their trade.

Some months later, when my list had expanded by a few hundred and the 'waiting room' was full (two patients sitting in the hall of the house in which I lived), a young girl burst in and said, 'Come quickly, doctor. My brother's had an accident and is bleeding an awful lot.' Pleased to escape from a boring, one-sided consultation, I grabbed my midwifery bag (the one with all the tools in) and crossed the road to the house opposite. There, on the floor of the back room, lay a small boy and his sister had not exaggerated when she said he was bleeding an awful lot. He had fallen, and when trying to save himself, had stuck his arm through the French window and severed, what I imagined to be, his axillary artery. Nothing was visible through the pool of blood pulsating in the axilla, so blindly I shoved in every Spencer Wells forceps I had, clamped them, and miraculously the bleeding stopped. A bit longer and he would have been completely exsanguinated. Mercifully, the ambulance arrived and whisked the little fellow off with all my Spencer Wells's dangling from him. I asked the ambulance man if he could see that I got my forceps back and, touchingly enough, he called at the surgery a few days later and returned them. The little lad survived, but was left with an Erbs Palsy (the waiter's 'tip' position). This involves the rotation of the hand on the forearm with the palm pointing upwards, brought about by damage to one of the axillary nerves, for example a crush injury – such as being squeezed by a Spencer Wells forceps!

The Brigadier

Saturday morning surgery, empty waiting room, a man came in 20 minutes late. I drew myself up to my full 5ft 6in, about to launch into a pompous spiel about hanging around for the likes of those who have plenty of time on their hands, when something made me change my mind. He looked down at me from about 6ft 2in with a steely look that made me realise that this was not a man to be trifled with and who was unaccustomed to taking orders. I courteously ushered him in. Just as well; he was a retired Brigadier, and a Doctor of Medicine to boot. He also played to a 2 handicap. When we got to know each other better, he invited me to call him Tom, which I did, and continued to do so with the greatest difficulty. Even *not* standing to attention did not come easily. His hips made him pack up golf and he very generously gave me his set of 'Henry Cotton' clubs.

The Damp Pyjamas

The nice old gent had passed away. The district nurse, the wife and myself stood by.

'Shall we put some nice clean pyjamas on him?' said the DN, indicating a new pair on the chest of drawers.

'We can't use those,' said the wife, 'they haven't been aired.'

The Black Stethoscope

Before the days of mobile phones and recorded messages, one used to leave one's telephone number when off the spree, so that contact was possible. One night, I was playing the saxophone in a band, as was my usual Tuesday habit, when I got a call. Leaving the band one short, I sped off dutifully. En route, I realised that I did not have my bag of tools with me, but had to pass the house where my presence was requested before I got back to the surgery. Taking a chance, and guessing the reason the call was made, I called at the house and, as suspected, the patient had expired. One has to do something to justify one's presence. I was still wearing my saxophone strap, hoping, to all present, that it would sufficiently resemble the conventional badge of office. By good chance it was black.

Dr. Skinner

Wife Beaters

To my surprise, they both came to the surgery, she with a really good black eye which she said had been administered by her husband. He made no attempt to deny this, but sat looking down meekly at his size 12 boots. Don't ask me, however, how a 16-stone, 6ft 4in and 3ft wide docker can look meek. He was huge, and not the sort of chap you would argue with unless you had a cocked, 12-bore shotgun in your hands. In the fond, but possibly mistaken belief that a stethoscope would offer protection, rather like a crucifix protects you from a vampire, I told him what I thought of him and urged his wife to get the police if there was a further assault. She was a very pretty, delicate-looking lady.

A few weeks later, the front door bell rang at about 11pm (my surgery was in the house in which I lived). I opened it to reveal our 6ft 4in docker looking as if he had fought a tiger and lost. He had deep scratches down both cheeks, a busted lip and blood streaming from his nose.

'Thought you might like to see why I have to belt the wife occasionally, doctor,' he said. The comparatively few wife beaters I have known have come from various strata of society. One of the worst was a posh sort of chap who was something in the City. Collar and tie, and shiny shoes. I urged his wife to get first the police and then a solicitor. Wives are usually too frightened to 'blow the whistle' for fear of reprisals, but on this occasion it helped. A burly sergeant came round, saw his nibs and suggested that he joined an evening class to give him a different interest, like flower arranging or playing the guitar, and then said that if he heard any more from his good lady, he would come round personally and make the chap wish he had joined an unarmed combat class. This event was in the 1960s. You wouldn't get away with that now. He'd get a crash course in counselling.

Yet another wife beater started on his mother after the wife left, as she got fed up with the 'banged into a door' story at work.

The Marx Brothers

I was called to a house one night by a neighbour who reckoned that murder was about to take place in the flat upstairs. Duly reporting for action, I found the husband reeling around, very drunk, shouting and swearing, threatening to wreck the home and kill the wife who, understandably, was backing off very skilfully, dodging between the sofa and the dining table. Managing to calm the situation a little, the wife and I sat on the sofa. Our friend sat opposite, holding an empty bottle by the neck, looking crest-fallen, but not for long. He suddenly got up and stood over me with the bottle raised high. He was a weedy sort of chap and didn't pose much of a physical threat. Nonetheless, in such a situation, one has to be ready to preserve one's cranium. The television was on behind him and a Marx Brothers film was showing. It was either *A Night at the Opera* or *Duck Soup*. In any event, Groucho was making some outrageous remark to a well-endowed lady in evening dress and lots of pearls and, although the sound was off, I knew well what he was saying. Quite involuntarily, the corners of my mouth curled up and, despite a massive effort to control them, I sat there with what appeared to be an idiotic half-grin on my face. He stared at me in disbelief.

'What's so bloody funny?' he shouted, and raised the bottle to the full extent of his backswing. Just as suddenly, he broke down, deflating like a pricked balloon, dissolving in tears of remorse, saying he never meant anyone no 'arm. His wife forgave him instantly and he replaced my seat on the sofa.

I left in a hurry to get back home to see the rest of the Marx Brothers' film.

The Dog

Again, late one night, the doorbell rang and there stood a young girl holding a large dog dripping quite a lot of blood onto my front doorstep. I managed to get a plastic sheet down before admission, as blood on your best Axminster is difficult to get off. This dog had jumped through a window, shattered it and cut a large chunk of himself on the inside of his thigh. The gash was about 4in long and, as dogs have veins that run in the substance of the skin, a suture job was indicated in the very near future. As luck would have it, my midwifery bag was in the hall and, as I threaded a suture needle, it occurred to me that our canine friend might not like to be stitched up. The young maiden assured me that he was a very good dog and she would take care of the sharp end if I did the necessary further down. True to her word, Fido remained very passive as I ran a mattress suture in the appropriate area and, to my delight, the bleeding stopped.

The next day the maiden called again and gave me half a crown (approx. 25p). She said she felt she shouldn't bother me again, but would go to the vet to have the stitch removed.

I subsequently learned that it is illegal for doctors to treat animals, but is legal for vets to treat humans.

The Bird I Taught to Fly

A big, black crow was walking about aimlessly in the garden. Although big, he was obviously a baby as he had a rounded, fluffy head unlike the flatter head of the adult. Also, the adults are very timid, yet you can approach babies as they have not yet discovered what a wicked lot of people there are around. My concern was a large cat hiding in the heather in the crouch position and wagging his tail in a pre-pounce way. I approached our feathered friend and, to my surprise, he let me pick him up. I threw him up in the air assuming he would take off out of harm's way, but he crash-landed a yard or two away. Puss was, by now, looking very happy at what he thought was a sitting duck (crow). I picked the bird up again, and throwing him skywards as vigorously as I could, I commanded him to fly in my most authoritative voice. He did, and disappeared into the wide blue yonder.

The Dundee Cake Tin

There may be those amongst you who recall the Dundee cake tin. A yellowish coloured tin about 8in across and 4in deep. Yet another old gent had departed this mortal coil. A real gent who had suffered a long illness and who had been cared for by his landlady. She had cooked for him, washed him, did his washing, and nursed him for many months. She had even laid him out, having been a nursing auxiliary at some time.

It is all too frequent for relatives, whom one didn't know existed, to come out of the woodwork in similar circumstances and go through the dearly departed's possessions like vultures. They leave their posh cars outside, and may even have the effrontery to shed a tear. Well, after one lot had departed, the old landlady showed me the Dundee cake tin and, on removing the lid, displayed tightly packed ten bob (50p) and pound notes. I'd never seen so much money.

'What shall I do with this, doctor?' she said.

'Mr R,' I said, 'was always telling me how kind you were, and that without you he would have had to go into a home, and that he would like to leave you something after he had gone, and I think this is what he meant.'

I hope she did what I suggested, but she was such an honest and nice old lady, she may well have declared it.

GP Jog at Crystal Palace with friend from Devon

A Young Bobby

I was strolling back across Lambeth Bridge, having said my piece at the Magistrates Court in Horseferry Road. The first half of Lambeth Bridge is slightly uphill, not very much, but just sufficient to promote that old, familiar, constricting pain across the chest that makes you stop and take an unusual interest in the magnificence of the view up the Thames. I had been leaning on the parapet when a voice behind me said, 'Are you all right, sir?' Behind me was a young policeman wearing wire-framed glasses. Did he think I was going to jump over the top? Or did he have a clue that sometimes mature, well-nourished gentlemen get a touch of angina now and again? I assured him that I was OK and thanked him for his vigilance.

Don't talk to me about police brutality.

I used to do a bit of police work. Mostly because there aren't too many GPs willing to get out of bed and make some poor soul walk the line, or stand on one leg. It's all different now. A urine or blood test, and you're guilty. In days gone by, you elected to be tried by jury. In which case, all juries would sympathise with you on the basis of 'there but for the Grace of God go I'.

I should add that the Court attendance fees were very good.

All this reminds me of a very late call one night when a friend, also a patient, called and said he was incarcerated in a police station in Balham (remember 'Gateway to the South'?). He was, in fact, a good friend of Peter Sellers and, eventually, a brilliant author; his treatise of Brigitte Bardot is a classic. When I got to the police station, it was evident that he was extremely pissed, but his usual charming and poised self. I expected the police to provide the necessary gear to enable me to take the blood samples. If they wanted the test, they must provide the material. No such luck. Seizing on this, I was able to drop a name (senior policeman at the golf club) and thus acquired the necessaries. It did dilute the sentence a bit, but with three times over the limit, it's tricky. He and I went back to his house and cracked open a bottle of brandy. I left his

25

house at 8am for 9am surgery which, I am ashamed to say, was conducted unshaven, unwashed, and incompetently.

The Flagpole

This story is not for the faint-hearted. My own eyes water and my facial muscles contract whenever I think of it. YOU HAVE BEEN WARNED.

It concerns a young married couple holidaying in Spain. They'd had a hilarious evening with friends, drinking Spanish plonk and finishing up in their apartment to continue the party. They migrated to the balcony, where a yard or two away was the flagpole boasting the hotel colours. Our hero found this to be some sort of challenge and, fancying himself as a fireman, leapt out into the night, clutched the pole, and proceeded to descend very fast. Now, those of us familiar with flagpoles know that, on ground level, there is a metal tube bracketed to the pole to give it stability. Our friend had overlooked this, and his rapid descent caused him to be impaled on this metal support. The open end of the tube penetrated his perineum (the area between the anus and his testicles) and emerged at the umbilicus (belly button, if you didn't know). His friends sportingly went downstairs and, after deliberation, decided the only solution was to reverse the descent and lift him off upwards (my eyes are watering already).

Spanish casualty department: a fag-smoking doctor (?) cobbled up the wound in the perineum (remember where that is?) and that at the umbilicus. He saw me a week later in my surgery and I removed the stitches. I could not believe that a rusty iron tube, following the path that it did, managed to miss all the vital structures and, as you can imagine, there are quite a few along that pathway. No investigations were done, no infection occurred, and the patient seemed to take it all in his stride. Interestingly, he denied experiencing any pain, which is a tribute to the remarkable analgesic properties of alcohol.

The coda to this event is that he and his wife had been trying for a family for some years and a month or so later she conceived. The foregoing procedure is not, however, recommended as standard treatment for infertility.

I still have a photograph of the patient's underpants showing the neat punch-out hole in the perineal area. If you would like a copy, send an S.A.E.

Ice

A little lad was brought into casualty one Sunday night suffering from a severe attack of asthma. He was put into an oxygen tent and it was adequately controlled. Unfortunately, the oxygen had to be passed through an ice reservoir for maximum effect and the ice supplies were limited. To me, the obvious solution was to ring the police and explain our requirements. As expected, they were extremely helpful and went into action straight away. The next I heard was that there were emergency calls being made on the radio throughout Kent calling for emergency ice deliveries to be made to Ashford Hospital to save a boy's life.

Talk about overkill. Police cars came screaming up to the hospital with buckets of ice, commandeered from other hospitals, fish shops, refrigeration plants, etc. We had enough ice to sink the Titanic.

The little lad did very nicely and went home the next day, puzzled by the fact that he was a celebrity. As he went home, there was an arrival. The hospital chief administrator. He is the main man, and is responsible for pushing around more paper clips than anyone else. HE was steaming. Who, he demanded, was responsible for mobilising Kent constabulary to get requirements for a patient without his permission?

Mea culpa.

The interview with him was short. I think I spoiled his day. I do dislike office boys who interfere with matters that do not concern them.

Maternal Demise

My mother had an arthritic hip, and was reduced to getting around on two elbow crutches. This was before the days of hip replacement surgery. Usually a very active and energetic lady, she developed new interests, namely: eating, looking at the television and drinking gin. Attempts to persuade her to take up other hobbies were abortive. Her weight ballooned, she became hypertensive, and was permanently on the brink of cardiac failure.

One very hard winter when power cuts were frequent, she was clearly unable to cope, so my wife and I had her transported to our house. The first night she improved dramatically and held court with the family who had gathered round. She was alert, humorous and happier than she had been for weeks. Next morning, alas, she was short of breath, distressed and a very unhealthy bluish colour. I called her doctor, a splendid chap who did his rounds with no more than a stethoscope and a prescription pad. 'Left ventricular failure,' he proclaimed. She needs morphia. This is clinically very correct, it relieves the patient's distress, calms their breathing and takes away the agony of not being able to get enough air into your lungs. The down-side to this, is that the patient may not survive. But at least they are comfortable and, if the heart is that bad, they are not going to do very well anyway.

'I'll get some morphia and come back,' said her GP.

'I've got some,' I volunteered. 'Would you like me to give it to her?'

Agreed.

I gave her the standard dose of 1/6 grains and very shortly after, her breathing became less desperate, her facial muscles relaxed and she was clearly not in distress.

Her heart stopped beating about an hour later.

Good clinical diagnosis and appropriate treatment. All the same, I wish it hadn't been me who pressed the plunger.

Murder and Suicide

I was called to a house one Saturday morning by a man and his wife who had just returned from shopping to find the wife's eighty-year-old father dead in his chair. Natural causes were assumed. Nonetheless, I sped round to see if there was anything useful I could do.

A uniformed policeman barred my way, despite my protestations. At that moment, two or three more police cars drew up and out poured a posse of plain clothes men. Apparently, after the call to me, the wife had gone upstairs and found her mother dead in the bath and, not unreasonably, called the police. Apparently her father had drowned his wife in the bath, gone downstairs and killed himself with an overdose of sleeping pills. The couple, both in their eighties, were always arguing and fought like cat and dog. The police said that this scenario is not as rare as one might think.

A week later the incident was reported in the local paper, with a photograph of a house labelled THIS WAS THE MURDER HOUSE. And whose house do you think had been photographed? MINE. My wife got quite twitched up about this, and swore that gawpers were walking past and viewing the crime scene. About three weeks later, the paper printed a disclaimer in very small print on the back page but one.

A dear old lady took a train to the West Country, specifically to take an overdose and kill herself. Her reason, her daughter told me, was that she didn't want the disgrace and embarrassment of doing it on her own home ground.

A newspaper reporter came in requesting a repeat prescription for his sleeping pills. He was a very nice man, and we used to have some very interesting chats. He had been having his prescription repeated for some time, and I had no reason to suspect anything unusual. He went straight home and took the lot and was found very dead the next morning. I felt bad about this and wished there had been some clue as to his state of mind. The presenting face obviously gives no clue as to what goes on inside the brainbox.

Daffodils

'You'd better come, doctor. Miss X has gone mad. She's locked herself in her room and is singing loudly. Also, she's been bringing in hundreds of daffodils all day.' Residents in the other flats were standing in the hall looking for excitement. I tapped on Miss X's door. 'Can I come in, Miss X? This is the doctor.' The singing stopped and the door opened a fraction. 'You can come in,' she said craftily, 'but no one else.' I slid in and she immediately shut and locked the door. I'd never seen anything like it. The room was strewn with daffodils, stuck round pictures and mirrors. The floor was carpeted with them and Miss X was clutching two large bunches and more were stuck in an array through her hair. Miss X then began the singing again and dancing round the room. To my horror, Miss X was stark naked. They never told us what to do in this sort of situation at medical school. You will never believe this, but I really cannot remember how it all worked out, it really was too much for me. What I do remember was the ambulance man taking her away, she was now wearing a dressing gown, and giving me a half grin and wink.

A Blue Phone Call

My wife was helping me one Thursday afternoon at my ante-natal clinic. The phone rings and she answers it, which is what she is there for. I am aware, after a minute or two, that she isn't talking, so I emerge from behind the screen to see what's happening. She is looking astonished and incredulous and frantically waves me away. I go back to the patient and come out again after another lengthy pause. Same scenario. I go away and give her another few minutes, and at last she hangs up.

'What was all that about?' I ask. She was looking rather pink about the ears and a bit breathless.

She says, 'I've just had an obscene phone call.'

'Wouldn't it have been better to hang up?' I suggested.

'No, the engineer kept intercepting and telling me that he knew I was getting an obscene call, but "please hang on and keep listening as we need time to trace the call".'

The wife fell for it hook, line and sinker. I was very suspicious and rang the engineers, who assured me that in no way did they adopt that procedure and that my wife had been the victim of a scam.

In spite of my annoyance, I felt a tinge of admiration for

the ingenuity of the perpetrators. How else to keep the conversational ball rolling? Mark you, you've got to have a good mate to help you, and one with similar interests.

Ladies, you have been warned!

Mushrooms

She was young, pretty and French. With the aid of a phrase book and dictionary she told me she had an itch 'down below'. At least I hoped that was what she told me, or I was in deep trouble. I called in my receptionist and explained the need to do an examination – 'down below'. It was quite apparent that this young lady had thrush. A benign condition with no nasty associations, and common enough among young women. Interestingly enough, it is a condition that responds quite well to locally applied yoghurt. Indeed I have been asked if the fruit flavoured variety will do.

Back in the surgery, I tell our Mademoiselle that she has thrush. Puzzled, she leafs through the dictionary and looks up in astonishment and says, 'Un oisseau? I'm in trouble now. 'No, no, no' I tell her, 'it's nothing to do with birds, it's a fungus'. More leafing through the dictionary, she looks up in alarm, 'Champignons?' I wish I'd stuck to monilia, but that's not in the phrase book. I prescribed appropriately and hoped the chemist knew more French than me. His name was Patel.

Not that it applies in this instance, but the Continentals use a lot of their medication in suppository form. We English are not too keen on this form of administration and prefer the oral route. Mark you, the rectal route has a lot to be said for it. It permits rapid absorption into the blood stream via a willing mucosa and by bypassing the stomach, allows things to be used that would otherwise cause gastric irritation, or indeed be destroyed by the gastric acid.

Furthermore, I think I would get some funny looks if old Mrs. Bloggs came in complaining of headaches and I said, 'Well, as soon as it comes on, pop one of these up your back passage.'

The Hangman

He was a Warrant Officer in the regular Army and was stationed somewhere up North shortly after the war.

He told me this story one day in surgery when we should have been talking about the actual reason he came to see me. He and a fellow W.O. used to meet a couple of civilians once or twice a week and play snooker, but periodically one of them used to disappear for a week or so. 'Where does Albert get to?' was the question. 'Didn't you know?' He's Albert Pierrepoint, the public hangman, and has to nip out to Nuremburg where they are having the War Crimes' trials and dangle a few convicted Nazis. The games of snooker were never quite the same after we learned this, as we felt a bit uneasy if we beat them. Not that Albert ever spoke about his work, or gave any clue as to what he did. He was a very quiet, agreeable man with a pleasant manner. I subsequently read that his father and grandfather were in the same business and that he felt he should carry on the family tradition and that it was a duty.

When Albert retired, he took over a pub and it was alleged that there was a brass plate on the counter saying, 'No hanging about the bar'. This I can assure you is not true. Nor were some of the alleged names, like the Last Drop Inn, The Noose and Gibbet, Hangman's Hideaway or The Trap Door Inn, etc.

The Lord Napier

The Lord Napier

You may recall from the MURDER & SUICIDE section that the local newspaper printed a large photo of my house and proclaimed it to be the Murder House, as a result of which, I requested a disclaimer. Papers are very slow to issue disclaimers and I purchased many copies before it appeared. My wife, however, noticed a small advert looking for musicians to start a big band at the local evening class. This, I felt, was going to be my big breakthrough. We duly presented ourselves and found that this embryo 'big band' was five strong. My wife, a concert pianist, was put on the drums and I was awarded the second trumpet chair, to be played on clarinet!

The years passed by and we got better and attracted some good players. My wife was promoted to keyboard and I got the second saxophone chair. We secured a 'gig' at a pub called the Lord Napier at Thornton Heath for a session on Wednesday night, which was a bit of luck as it was my half day. We were, by this time, a full sixteen-piece band (with vocalist) doing the classics of yesteryears: Benny Goodman, Tommy Dorsey, Duke Ellington; vocals by Frank Sinatra, Dean Martin, Tony Bennet, et alia. Stiffened by some ex-professionals, we were pretty good, and indeed some nights there were more in the audience than in the band.

I'd agreed to be involved as the venue was well off my professional patch, but one night the inevitable happened. I looked up and there sitting in the front row, about two yards away, was a quartet of my patients, apparently nudging each other saying, 'Yes, it is him! I'm sure it's him.' And sure enough it was. My secret was out. I joined them in the interval and they treated me like a celebrity. Except that I bought the drinks, which cost me a jolly sight more than the £1 I earned for my musical services. Mark you, I would have paid the guy who ran it a fiver for the sheer pleasure of playing in the band.

We kept that 'gig' for about twelve years, until a new manager gave us the elbow, thinking we were a bit common. He didn't last long and music was restored. By then it was too late and we were all doing other things. But I still have my Lord Napier tie.

Retirement Gifts

Carbon Monoxide

At the height of a flu epidemic, one may collect as many as 20 house visits a day. When you add this to surgeries twice daily, dental anaesthetic sessions, clinics and other odd things likely to crop up, it makes for a very busy time. 12 to 14 hours a day is not exceptional. Throw in the odd baby being born at night and after a couple of weeks, you are punch drunk and running on auto pilot. This sort of pattern probably accounts for my intolerance of those who get stressed out when the boss ticks them off for some minor offence.

One does one's best to vet the calls for home visits and hopes one gets it right. Fortunately, the call to a family of five was accepted. Mother, father, son, daughter, and a few weeks old baby. Punch drunk or not, I must have had a few grey cells still working because the whole scene was very odd. They were all very quiet and pale, except the baby who was yelling her head off due to being neglected. None of the family had the strength to get up and do the necessary. They were not febrile and sweating and, although the temptation to say 'flu' and move on to the next household was great, I decided that something was very wrong, but didn't know what it was. I sent the whole family into hospital. Not an easy task to get a family of five admitted at a time when hospitals were bulging at the doors and it was standing room only.

They were all back home two days later, fit and recovered. You'll never guess, CARBON MONOXIDE POISONING. They had a crack in their boiler heating system and the deadly gas was seeping into all the rooms. Being winter, all hatches were battened down and there was no air to dilute the toxin. The room where the baby slept was on a different pipeline, so escaped.

Interestingly, there had been no smell of fumes (carbon monoxide is odourless anyway) and the family were PALE. Carbon Monoxide is associated with an unnaturally high colour.

I Throw Away a Fortune

One of my patients with whom I became quite friendly, as he was a very useful handyman, motor mechanic and 'Jack of all trades', brought me a set of transparency photographs of a very tasty lady dressed, or rather undressed, in very sexy lingerie, some of which were topless. Dismantling a garden shed, as instructed, he had come across these pictures which he (understandably) retained, despite the instruction to burn the dismantled shed and its contents. He was at a loss to know what to do as the lady concerned was in the process of marital severance. This I knew, but I also knew that she was having a torrid love affair with a senior member of the government. Also, one of her previous amours had been a professional photographer. This, of course, accounted for the excellence of the quality of the photos. I must stress that the pics were not pornographic, but teasing representation of the sort of thing we see daily on 'page three'. Nonetheless, these, and the story that went with them, would be worth a king's ransom to certain publications at the time.

Their affair became public a year or two later, which would have been the perfect time to give myself early retirement, a villa in the South of France, and an Aston Martin. So what did I do? Made a pyre in the back garden, poured on a little paraffin and watched it all go up in smoke. At least I can sleep at night.

My Uncle

Many years ago my daughter was performing in an 'am dram' production of *South Pacific* and, for some unaccountable reason, invited an uncle of mine to accompany my wife and me.

The first half went off OK and we were into the 'Some Enchanted Evening' bit when my uncle emitted a quiet, grunting sound. I looked at him and his eyes were closed and there was a patina of sweat on his forehead. His breathing was so shallow that it was difficult to see if he was breathing at all. His pulse was very thin and I was not sure I could really feel it.

I actually thought he was dead, or at least very near it. What to do? There we were, sitting there in Row L, and about six people in from the gangway. I whispered to the chap next to me, 'My relative has collapsed and I have to get him out, pass it on'. It was a bit like that Christmas party game, 'Chinese Whispers', when you say something to the person next to you and by the time it does the circuit, it comes back as something completely different. However, the chap did it right and the four or five people concerned moved into the gangway. Next problem – how to get an unconscious, large man out of a theatre seat and transport him to the back of the auditorium. More 'Chinese Whispers' to the two behind – fortunately seating a couple of muscular young men who caught on very quickly and passed my uncle along the row and laid him in the gangway. 'Can you help me get him out?' I hissed, and the four of us manhandled him clumsily out to the box office area. We all stood looking down on uncle. One bloke said, 'He looks a goner to me,' and another said, 'I didn't think the show was all that bad.'

Local hospital casualty department … young houseman diagnoses heart attack and says we must do some tests. By now, uncle was showing signs of survival. He sat up and asked for a glass of water, and in two minutes, seemed back to normal. He insisted on going home, and was as right as rain the next day.

He survived a good few years, and died when he had an accident in his garden. So what it was all about, I really don't know.

Retirement removing plate

Hadrian's Wall

If you want to get a buzz and a real feeling of 'being there', go to Hadrian's Wall and explore the museums along its length and walk along some of the bits that are left. You can keep the Sphinx and the pyramids.

Day 1: My wife and I stopped for lunch at a restaurant by the side of a lake. After the egg and chips, I saw an ambulance draw up and begin working on a prostrate young man. These situations are tricky. Usually, the paramedics are very good at accidents and can outgun a GP on holiday. However, I thought

I should put in a casual appearance, standing well back and see if there was any contribution I could make.

They were doing mouth-to-mouth and cardiac resuscitation on a young man who looked very dead. I watched for a while and stepped in, asking if I could help. They were very pleased to see me, as they have to continue resuscitation until a doctor certifies death, which wasn't difficult in this case.

I never learned the details, but apparently he had been for a swim after a big fry-up meal, washed down with a few tins of lager. To see a young man dead just because he was clowning about was very sad.

Day 2: Motoring along by the side of a vallum, we encountered a multiple car crash. A vallum, incidentally, is a constructed ditch behind a Roman fortification. Three cars were involved and there were about six or seven casualties lying in the grass being attended to by seemingly competent adults. I did my usual trick of standing well back and assessing the situation. Another car drew up and out hopped a bespectacled lady in functional tweeds who descended on the battlefield with the traditional cry of, 'Stand back, I'm a doctor!' One of the attendants looked up, pointed to another and said, 'He's a consultant orthopaedic surgeon,' indicated another and said, 'He's a consultant anaesthetist, and I'm a surgical registrar.'

I think in future the good lady will do what I do, and stand on the fringe for a while.

The only time I've pulled rank was at a road accident at the junction of Thurlow Park Road and Croxted Road, London. A young man in a mini had hit something pretty thoroughly and catapulted himself into the back seat. He was wedged tight in the corner with his legs draped over the back of the front seat. His neck was severely flexed and his chin pressing on his sternum. Breathing was restricted and he was turning a delicate shade of blue. The Mini door was jammed, but gave up the unequal struggle when one of my powerful neighbours (the same one who found the girlie photos in the garden shed) intervened. I was able to get in and drag our friend into a position that did not embarrass his respiration. 'Don't move him!' cried a spectator, trying to restrain me. 'I'm a St John's First Aid man.' 'And I'm a doctor,' I said, 'so I outrank you.'

The Soft Machine (1960s)

One morning, four young men came into the surgery to register. They had shoulder length hair, flared jeans, high heeled cowboy boots and one wore bright orange beads. This was quite unusual in suburbia. It was the early days of the 'Groups' and few people had actually seen the real thing close to, especially in a doctor's waiting room. It transpired that they were a pop group and were living in the house of the drummer's mother, who at the time was a celebrated broadcaster with the BBC. They were an extremely nice group of young men, all well educated and they called themselves The Soft Machine. I had the privilege of hearing them rehearse, and was astonished by their musicianship and the depth of musical knowledge. Unfortunately, this is not what the teenagers want, and they are the ones who buy the recordings and therefore dominate the charts. They were too good for the charts. The Beatles at this time were churning out simple four chord tunes until their manager, George Martin, suggested modifications which resulted in good stuff like 'Eleanor Rigby', 'Fool on the Hill' and 'Michelle'.

The Soft Machine were too good. Their progressive pop inventions appealed mostly to people with taste, discernment and musicians. Charlie Parker, John Coltrane and Miles Davies suffered a similar fate. They were geniuses, but too far ahead of their time to cash in.

The Soft Machine went to France as the Machine Molle, and were big time there and in the whole of Europe. Unfortunately, their drummer had an accident, broke his back and finished up in a wheel chair. He then went on to keyboard and became a brilliant player, rather surprising as drummers are not usually rated as the subtlest of musicians.

A young lady comes into morning surgery in a full ball gown, crumpled silk stole, drooping corsage and looking decidedly the worse for wear. She had a grossly infected throat and must have been feeling awful. Other patients in the waiting room must have been confused, until they learned that she had come straight from the Chelsea Arts Ball.

This time, during evening surgery, in comes an attractive, well upholstered young lady, showing about 4in of eye-catching cleavage.

'Excuse my dress, doctor, but I'm going from here to a fancy dress party. I'm going as Nell Gwynne.'

I played it dead pan and resisted the temptation to make a remark about oranges.

The Receptionist

After a few years in general practice, working on my own, I realised that much of my surgery time was wasted answering the phone and filling in forms. The answer was obvious. Get a receptionist. I didn't advertise, but asked around, and a patient I knew quite well said she thought she knew the ideal person. An interview was set up, and along came Julie. My wife looked very disapprovingly at this stunning apparition and I could not resist a jaw breaking grin. She was very pretty, with a bouffant hair style, heavy make up (à la Dusty Springfield), a mini skirt, black tights (I think) and high heeled shoes. I would have given her the job straight away, but my wife, understandably, was a little hesitant. 'She'd look more the part in a massage parlour,' she said afterwards. However, it will not be a surprise that Julie got the job.

She was an extremely nice girl, very nice to the patients and good on the phone and was saving me a lot of time. She lived locally and she and her parents knew most of the patients, which made them feel more comfortable. My wife, however, was still not too happy about the skirt length. 'Doesn't look very professional,' she said. So with some reluctance, I despatched Julie to a shop in The Edgware Road where they dispensed doctors and nurses uniforms, boiler suits, chef's gear, etc.

Julie told me that evening in surgery, that she had done the necessary and would start wearing her purchases the next morning. Tap on the door, and in comes Julie. Well, I nearly dropped my stethoscope and burst out laughing. She looked sensational. Instead of a knee length, conventional white coat, she'd bought a physiotherapist's coat with a high clerical collar, short sleeves, diagonal fastening buttons down the front and finishing in length just below the waist and far from disguising the short skirt, it seemed to make it look shorter.

Julie was such a nice girl that I, nor indeed my wife, had the heart to tell her that she'd got it all wrong. Not surprisingly, there were never any complaints.

No Smoking

A very well educated, elderly maiden lady had died and the police had been called to gain access. Inevitably, I was called and there was a resumé as to her general medical health and lifestyle. There were no suspicious circumstances. At this point, one of the policemen took out a packet of fags and was preparing to light up.

This annoyed me and I told him that Miss X didn't approve of smoking, particularly in her flat.

He gave me a funny sort of look, as if to say, 'What on earth does it matter?'

I smiled at him and he smiled at me. 'Sorry,' he said and put his fag back in the packet.

Nitrous Oxide

This gas is an anaesthetic, a very light anaesthetic, only suitable for very short periods of time and light surgery. It comes into its own in dentistry when you want patients in and out quickly and not cluttering up the place needing long periods of time to recover. It is popularly known as 'laughing gas'. I have no idea why because, having given hundreds of administrations, I have yet to hear anyone laugh.

Admittedly, there is an excitatory phase when a patient is coming round. When the subject becomes very restless and may thresh about for a short time. The candidates most likely to need restraining are sailors, firemen, and the very worst are the tough-looking types who come in whistling; these are trying to hide their terror at the pending ordeal. Occasionally, they resort to swearing. The worst I ever heard was a priest with a tirade that would have made a taxi driver blush. The patient, on regaining consciousness, has no recollection of their vocal expertise. My father was a dentist and on qualifying, taught me the gentle art of doing 'gases'. I earned a fee for my efforts which was very handy in the bleak days.

We used to do a marathon session on a Saturday morning, about 12 to 15 patients, some of whom were there for extractions of the whole lot. This was not uncommon in those days due to a condition known as pyorrhoea when the gums are heavily diseased and the fangs discoloured and unsightly. You had to work very fast to extract 20 or more teeth in the allotted time. They flew around like machine gun bullets, hitting the walls, the operator, the anaesthetist (me) and on more than one occasion, the ceiling. The patient was rewarded with an immediate set of gleaming white choppers (previously prepared) and a mirror in which to admire himself. Never a woman. Why? One of our customers was one of our golfing four, to give you an idea of the rapid recovery, he was with us on the first tee at 2pm.

I was casualty surgeon (now known as A & E) and used to reduce fractures under nitrous oxide. You used to have to wait for a consultant anaesthetist to come in from a neighbouring hospital, who would reluctantly come in, resenting giving his services for a junior house officer. He would floor the patient with Pentothal, needing three hours for recovery time when the procedure required only a few seconds. This was impractical, as in the winter and icy conditions, wrist fractures were almost queuing up. My technique was to get the nurse to hold the mask, take it off again at the magic point, and I would reduce the fracture during the recovery phase. The patient would walk home in quarter of an hour. Inevitably, the word got back to the 'paper clip pushers' who descended on me, forbidding my efforts to give an anaesthetic and do the operation. You can't argue with people like these. Ultimately, it's the patient who suffers.

Going back to dentistry for a moment. After I gave up smoking, I developed a very sweet tooth and would have to stop on my rounds to get my blood sugar up with a Mars bar or two. This did two things, my weight increased by two stone and my teeth began to dissolve (giving me frequent bouts of toothache), necessitating visits to my father with the request, 'Whip this one out for me guv'nor, please.' Very shortly after, I would be back on duty visiting the sick. There is nothing clever or heroic about this, it was the way it was.

After my father's retirement, I got that old familiar pain again (I still had a few teeth left) and decided on a DIY job. He had left me a few dental forceps and I sat down in front of a mirror. I have never had 50,000 volts put through me, but I felt it was a fair comparison after the first tug. What about some anaesthetic? Good idea! Half a tumbler of Scotch and four Anadins later, I had another go and knocked the voltage down to about 10,000. 'Come on,' I said to myself soothingly, hiccoughing quietly. 'It can't be all that bad.' 'Oh, yes it bloody well is,' I said back to myself, closed my eyes and pulled. There it was, proudly held in the forceps, with a nice little abscess on the apex. Never tell me any secrets, because if the nasty guys came at me with the cattle prod, I'd sing like the proverbial canary.

Heimlich Manoeuvre

If you happen to be in a restaurant with your beloved, or other, and there is a happy and noisy party at the next table, laughing and joking. When suddenly one of the guests gets up wearing an anxious expression, looking distressed, and hurries towards the 'gents'. Without your help he is probably going to die. In a moment of jollification, while chewing on a tough bit of steak and attempting to insert a brilliant bit of riposte into the conversation, he has confused his reflexes at the moment of swallowing and got the foreign body stuck in his windpipe.

Naturally, you recognise the emergency straight away and follow him poste haste to the loo. He will be bending over the basin, his breathing will be stertorous, and he will be turning a delicate shade of blue. You approach him from behind, put your arms round his waist and (bunching your hands together and holding them just below his sternum) you give the most almighty jerk, if nothing happens, you do it again and then again. If it's your (or more to the point, his) lucky day, a bolus of steak will be propelled forcibly on to the mirror above the basin, and instantly the subject returns to normal. He gives you a curt nod, washes his hands, and returns to his party. You go back and resume your candlelit dinner … no one, not even the victim, knows what happened. So don't expect any reward.

Apparently, there are a small number of deaths that happen annually in this way. So watch it. I, personally, have never experienced this scenario, and hope I never will. What I have experienced, however, which is ten times more frightening, is an emergency tracheotomy.

Dr. & Mrs. Skinner

Emergency Tracheotomy

In the chimpanzee and higher apes, the mandible (lower jaw) is longer than in man, and therefore can accommodate thirty-two teeth. Sixteen up and sixteen down. In man, however, the jaw gets smaller, but the number of teeth is the same. This, not surprisingly, leads to overcrowding and the dentist has to remove four perfectly good teeth, so that the subject does not have an irregular line of fangs.

The subject of this story is a five-year-old-boy. I was giving the gas, and my father was doing the extractions. The little lad was very co-operative, and the induction smooth. The first three teeth were removed, then the fourth. 'It's pipped!' proclaimed my father. Now 'pipping' is self-explanatory. It's the same as squeezing an orange pip between finger and thumb and the pip can be projected for quite a distance with some force. In this instance, the tooth had shot to the back of the throat, somehow got behind the pack, and lodged in the windpipe. We were in serious trouble. The little lad turned blue, his breathing laboured and noisy. Over the shoulder, banging on his back, and a fruitless attempt to reach the tooth, which was stuck firmly in the upper windpipe.

He was going to die, unless he could get some air in his lungs. Words came floating back from a surgical tutorial many years ago. 'Make sure you start your initial incision well below the thyroid cartilage, because if you wreck the vocal cords, and they survive, they'll take you to the cleaners. Also, look out for an aberrant artery crossing the midline and joining the two carotid arteries.'

With this reassuring advice, I was given a scalpel, and really not knowing what the hell I was doing, I made a deep incision in the belief that I was hastening the little chap's end more than saving him. I think on that day, old Hippocrates, or the good Lord himself were guiding my hand, for suddenly the trachea (windpipe) came into view. Easily recognised by the cartilaginous rings which keep it open. What do we do now? I had no tracheotomy tube, so how to get air into the lungs? At this point the patient was on the floor and I was kneeling by his side. I made a two centimetre, transverse incision between the tracheal rings, reversed the scalpel and put the handle in the incision and twisted.

Air rushed into the lungs and the sound was like a Mozart Symphony. We were some way through the wood, but by no means out of it. The ambulance arrived at that point and to save time, my father carried the patient out while I kept the handle of the scalpel in situ. The Saturday morning shoppers parted, screaming at the grisly spectacle. We sped up the Downham Way flat out, with bells ringing and tyres squealing. A and E took over and my father and I were suddenly surplus to requirements.

Thoughtfully, the nurse brought the car up to the hospital to take us back to the surgery. In our blood-stained gowns, I don't think they would have let us on the tram.

We all looked at each other, took a deep breath and knocked back half a tumbler of Scotch.

My father said, 'Ring the Club, nurse, and cancel our golf match.'

The patient survived in spite of further problems. The Ear,

Nose and Throat Department, attempting to extract the tooth via the mouth, had the misfortune to push it further down the trachea when it slid past my DIY incision, down the left main bronchus (it's always the left) causing the lung to collapse. Next stop, the thoracic surgeons who opened up the chest, having removed a rib, removed the tooth from the bronchus.

That little fellow must have been real tough to survive that lot. But they breed them that way in Bellingham (viz Henry Cooper).

My father was supported by the Dental Defence Union, and I by the Medical equivalent. They warned us that under no circumstances were we to get in touch with the patient or his family as a Court case would be pending. We were obviously interested and sympathetic, and by devious means we learned that he was doing well.

It may be of passing interest to note that the annual fee to be a member of the Defence Union in the 1960s was £2. In 2006 it was over £2000.

The Court Case

About a year later, my father and I were instructed to see a legal wise-man in the Inns of Court as the case was being given an airing. We were ushered into a murky, unbelievably untidy room, which (I was told) were chambers. There was the wise-man, sitting on a huge leather throne. My father and I were seated on sensible chairs about six inches lower than the throne. This, we gathered, was to ensure that we knew our place in his legal world. The wise-man, having done a bit of homework, sat back in his throne, steepled his fingers (exposing an egg stain on his waistcoat) and said, 'They haven't got a case, give them £25 to have a day at the seaside.'

Another year passed by, and a day was set for the battle to commence. We were introduced to two youngish men, who appeared to be familiarising themselves with the case for the last five minutes. These were our representatives and defenders. When we got into court, they were sitting in row B. Sitting in row A was a very impressive looking gent in a gown and wig. Just like *Rumpole of the Bailey*. He was the opposition and a Q.C. Our chaps were 'juniors' and had to call him 'sir.' The judge seemed to get on very well with 'Rumpole', but treated our pair as it they were junior house surgeons. My father and I had an expert witness in the form of a consultant anaesthetist. The opposition had a geriatric registrar. A rather unprepossessing chap, of dubious experience in any particular field.

This all sounds a bit sneaky, but, understandably, the profession tends to close ranks when a colleague is in trouble, and is not very forthcoming when they have to go to court and criticise the misfortunes of others. 'There but for the grace of God, etc.'

Strangely, the judge took a shine to this chap and hung on to his every, critical word. My father went into the dock and got a terrible grilling from the bloke who was supposed to be on our side. The 'Rumpole' chap, however, was extremely sympathetic and courteous. Very confusing. Our expert witnesses were never called, neither was I. Quite suddenly the judge made up his mind and terminated the proceedings. 'I respect that Mr Skinner has served the public well for many years, but in this instance I feel there was a lack of judgement. I award £7,000 damages'. My father has had a few knocks in his life, but this was really one in the solar plexus. We were all stunned by the suddenness of the decision. To be fair, I think the damages were reasonable; after all you don't expect to have a tooth out and finish up at the wrong end of a thoracic surgeon's scalpel. It would have been kinder to have explored the events in greater detail, and not to have made it seem like a careless act.

The plaintiffs were over the moon and asked the judge if they could have an advance on the damages, so they could all go away on a nice, long holiday. 'No,' said the judge, 'Give him £5 for a nice, big Teddy Bear.'

Our Saturday morning gas sessions continued as usual for a

few more years but there was always that lurking feeling of apprehension. Sometimes lightening does strike twice in the same place.

One of the morals of this story is that if you ever find yourself in a similar situation, make sure you make a real nuisance of yourself and ensure you meet your representatives well before the case, and tell them what you want them to know. I got the impression that our Defence Unions either thought the case was a pushover, or hopeless. So much for our wise-man's offer of £25. Ha, bloody, ha!

We never saw or heard of the family again. They moved down to the coast. Good idea. Sea air would be better for the little lad's respiratory system than the high CO_2 emissions in Bellingham.

The Rome Restaurant

A young, nimble-minded patient bought a moored barge on the Embankment called, I believe, *'The Nautilus'*. On it he constructed a restaurant called 'Hello Sailor'. It was not renowned for its culinary expertise but more for its waitresses who were dressed in saucy sailor hats, short pleated skirts and were all very pretty. At lunchtime it was bulging at the gangway by hordes of young, and not-so-young, office workers. This was sold; the next venture was in the City and was called 'School Dinners'.

It was again staffed by pretty girls but now dressed as *St Trinian's* pupils in short (very short) gymslips, black stockings and battered panama hats. There was a headmistress who could make you stand in the corner, wearing a dunce's cap, if you didn't eat your greens. In the more severe cases (if you were lucky) you got the cane. I never went there, but have it on good authority that that was the way it was.

My patient's next venture was in Fleet Street and called 'The Rome Restaurant'. He very kindly asked if I would like to go there one day for lunch. His parting words were 'Bring a friend, but not your wife'.

I took a worldly-wise colleague and we found 'The Rome Restaurant' opposite the old *Daily Express* offices. A very unpretentious 'hole' in the wall located down some steps entering into fantasy land. The place was done up like a Roman villa with a couple of pillars, plinths with busts of emperors and an actual working fountain. The walls were decorated with paintings of nymphs chasing nymphets through the shrubbery and Pegasus doing a four point landing on a patio. The focal point was the crescent-shaped bar across one corner. Careful observation showed that there was no flap and to get behind it, in order to dispense drinks, one had to mount a small two-step ladder and acrobatically climb over the bar. It didn't take long to work this one out. The waitresses (pretty) uniforms were the skimpiest and flimsiest togas ever beheld by a centurion. Gold sandals and a crown of laurel leaves completed the picture. The call for drinks was non-stop, and who cared if the steak was a little tough. My colleague and I were naturally very sparing with our requests.

The punters left about mid afternoon, leaving just my friend and me. We both experienced a vague feeling of unease when, fortunately, our host emerged and introduced us as doctors.

The scene suddenly changed. The girls clustered round and, previously having been cheeky and flirtatious, suddenly went into ordinary mode. In no time, we were discussing father's hernia, mother's gall stones and granny's arthritis. We were more comfortable now. We felt we had fulfilled our function, sung for our supper and no more would be expected of us. We left for suburbia in time for our five o'clock surgeries feeling slightly bewildered. We had lived in a fantasy world for a few hours, and to return to normality made us wonder if it ever really happened.

My patient's next venture was a restaurant in the Canary Islands. He went there as his wife suffered from rheumatoid arthritis and he thought the climate would suit her. I hope it did, because he died about two years later. Of what, I do not know.

Mizpah Issit

Fancy remembering a name like that! Jewish, I believe. This splendid, arthritic, octogenarian was virtually housebound. I used to pop in and see her from time to time to top up her pills, but mostly to listen to her fund of fascinating stories.

She used to be a dancer in the days of the music halls, when emporia like the Brixton Empress, Camberwell Palace and the New Cross Empire were the centres of entertainment. She was invariably on the same bill as Gertie Gitana, Dan Leno, The Chocolate Coloured Coon, Burlington Bertie and a young Gracie Fields. 'Our Gracie', while singing morale boosting songs to our troops going off to war, was packing her bags to go off to the safe haven of America. The reason she had to do this was because she married an Italian film director called Monty Bianchi and thus acquired Italian citizenship, making herself an alien. She was allowed limited use of a British passport to do a certain amount of troop entertainment, but things were never quite the same. She lost her status as Forces Sweetheart to Vera Lynn and left America after the war to live in Capri. She was, however, made a Dame and died on the Isle of Capri in 1979 aged 81. Despite her erstwhile popularity, there were those who could not stand her yodelling.

A friend of mine visited her grave on Capri and was quite upset to find it overgrown with weeds.

Now Mizpah had a huge picture hanging over her bed (34in

x 44in). I will tell you in a minute why these figures are so precise. It was called *'The Music Teacher'* and depicted an elegant, old man sitting by a grand piano. At the keys was a pretty young girl looking forlorn and downcast, obviously having trouble with C sharp minor, or some such. Along with *'Monarch of the Glen'*, *'When Did You Last See your Father?'* and *'A Stag at Bay'*, prints of these classics graced the walls of many a Victorian home, and were probably obtainable by sending up six Oxo cube cartons plus a penny for postage.

While Mizpah was chatting away, I would invariably be looking up at *'The Music Teacher'* and one day she said, 'You like that picture, don't you, doctor?' 'Er, yes!' I said, having a bad feeling as to where the conversation was going. 'Then, I want you to have it.' Mizpah was most insistent and I reluctantly agreed to come round after evening surgery (when I knew it would be dark).

About 9pm, I nervously drove round to Mizpah's, hooked the front door key on its string through the letter box and let myself in. Mizpah was out of bed, which was necessary as I would have to stand on the bed to get the picture down. Not so easy, as the bed was more like a trampoline. No disaster, however, and I skulked out into the night and loaded the masterpiece into the back of my Ford Popular. I was surprised by how furtively I was acting.

I cleaned the glass, restored the outer frame with black boot polish and the inner frame with gold paint, and behold, I had a masterpiece.

The reason for the accuracy of the measurements is that, while writing this story, I went and measured it where it still hangs today in my dining room. (Viewing by request.)
Thank you, Mizpah!

Afterword

I have been retired over ten years and for some unaccountable reason, I recently began to write some of my memories. As I wrote one, others came tumbling in and before long, I was churning them out at a rate that surprised me. I may have difficulty in remembering what I did yesterday, but the stories described came back with crystal clarity.

I hope they do not appear disrespectful in any way, nor, do I hope, show any sort of self-aggrandisement. The stories are as exactly as they were. There are many more, but I think these will do for starters.

My decision to be a GP was absolutely right. Where, in any other of the specialities, would you accumulate such a fund of events?

I recall one night, helping a dear old soul to pass comfortably from this world to the next, then going on to attend a confinement which produced a lovely, little seven pound girl. Dad comes in with a tray of tea, and mum, dad, the midwife and self, sitting and looking very pleased with ourselves. Not forgetting a little lad of three, peering in puzzlement at his recently acquired sister.

I go home in my Ford Popular car. Getting out, I reflect on a good night's work. Nature's work. Keep the balance. ONE-OUT, ONE-IN. The pavements are wet, the magic of the

Dawn Chorus is just starting, it's 4am and I must get a couple of hours sleep before 9am surgery.

I thank all my patients for the privilege of letting me be their family doctor.